Department of Transport

Code of Practice

SAFETY
OF LOADS
ON VEHICLES

LONDON: The Stationery Office

Applications for reproduction should be made in writing to The Copyright Unit, Her Majesty's Stationery Office, St Clements House, 2-16 Colegate, Norwich NR3 1BQ

First published 1972
Twelth impression 1997

ISBN 0 11 550666 7

CONTENTS

ACKNOWLEDGEMENTS

The following organisations and departments collaborated in the production of this revised Code of Practice.

Association of Webbing Load Restraint Equipment Manufacturers

Cordage Manufacturers Institute

Freight Transport Association

Health and Safety Executive

Metropolitan Police

Metropolitan Police Forensic Science Laboratory

Road Haulage Association

Road Transport Industry Training Board

Society of Motor Manufacturers and Traders

Department of Transport

SECTION 1. INTRODUCTION

1.1 Not only is it a legal requirement but it is commonsense to make sure that all loads carried on vehicles are adequately secured so that there is no likelihood of them moving or falling off with the very real possibility of danger to the driver and other road users. This applies to all vehicles and to all types of load. Loose objects or materials etc falling or blowing off open vehicles may not always be a danger but are likely to be at least a nuisance and at worst fatal. Remember, if a load either causes or is likely to cause danger or nuisance to people in the vicinity of the vehicle an offence might be committed—see Regulation 97 of the Motor Vehicles (Construction and Use) Regulations 1978 the text of which is given in Appendix A.

1.2 Sections 1—6 of this Code outline the general requirements and basic principles of load safety. Sections 7—14 provide advice, based on proven good practice, about satisfactory methods for securing the more common types of load.

1.3. Because of the extreme variety of loads, vehicles and operating conditions it is not possible to cover all the circumstances likely to be encountered by drivers and operators so the contents of this Code must not be regarded as exhaustive or exclusive. Satisfactory securing methods not mentioned in this Code are in existence and others will be developed in the future. However, the basic principles described in this Code must be complied with irrespective of the actual method used to secure the load.

1.4 In addition to the load safety methods described in this Code extra precautions are necessary when dangerous goods, eg toxic and corrosive chemicals and flammable substances, are carried on road vehicles. A list of the main regulations and approved Codes of Practice currently applicable to the carriage of these substances is given at Appendix B.

1.5 HIGH LOADS

Particular attention should be paid to the dangers of high loads that might have to pass under bridges or other structures across roads. Every year several hundred bridges are hit by lorries loaded too high or which are themselves too high to pass

1

underneath, resulting in some cases in both drivers and other people being killed or injured. Even a slight impact on a railway bridge can dislodge the rails which could result in a derailed train and many casualties.

It is already a requirement in Regulation 80A of the Motor Vehicles (Construction and Use) Regulations 1978, as amended by Amendment No 5 of 1978: SI 1978 No 1317, that skip carriers, engineering plant, and vehicles carrying containers, demountable bodies, and engineering equipment display the total travelling height of the vehicle in the cab if this height is over 12 feet (3.66 metres). Any driver of a high vehicle should watch for bridges and advance warning signs indicating the safe clearance height, and exercise extreme caution.

1.6 RO-RO FERRY OPERATIONS

The guidance given in this Code is intended to ensure the safety of loads on vehicles on the road taking into account acceleration, braking and cornering. However, when a vehicle is carried on a ship, as in roll-on, roll-off ferry operations, the vehicle and its load will be subject to different forces due to the rolling and pitching motions of the vessel, and hence a restraint system that is suitable for road use will often not be adequate at sea.

The Department of Trade Merchant Shipping Notice M849 (or any subsequent revision) gives some guidance on the securing of vehicles on ships and an indication of the forces likely to be encountered at sea. Vehicle operators intending to use ro-ro ferries should ensure that their load restraint systems are capable of withstanding such forces.

The securing of the vehicle to the ship is also important and the vehicles should therefore be fitted with lashing points that are, again, of adequate strength to withstand the forces likely to be encountered at sea and easily accessible to deck crews–not obstucted by fuel tanks, batteries etc. If necessary advice on this latter point should be sought from the ferry operators.

1.7 SUGGESTIONS FOR IMPROVEMENTS

Inevitably, as a result of further experience and a continual development of load securing systems, this Code of Practice will need to be periodically reviewed and amended. Suggestions for improving or adding to its content are welcomed and should be sent to:

The Department of Transport
Vehicle Standards and Engineering Division
2 Marsham Street
LONDON SW1P 3EB

SECTION 2. PRINCIPLES OF LOAD SAFETY

2.1 Forces are generated on the load when a vehicle brakes, accelerates, changes direction or crosses road undulations (see Figs 1 & 2).

These forces are frequently greater than the frictional restraint between the load and platform, therefore a load that is not secured by some form of restraining device *may not be secure*.

2.2 The forces acting on the load during braking increase with the rate of deceleration and the weight of the load. Therefore as braking efficiencies and payloads increase it becomes increasingly important that loads are adequately secured.

2.3 It requires much more force to stop a load which has started moving than it does to prevent movement in the first place. This 'battering ram' effect increases rapidly with the increase in distance through which the load moves relative to the vehicle. It is essential therefore that the load is restrained in such a way that movement relative to the vehicle is prevented.

2.4 The basic principle upon which this Code of Practice is based is that the combined strength of the load restraint system must be sufficient to withstand a force not less than the total weight of the load forward and half of the weight of the load backwards and sideways (see Fig 3). Vertical movements may occur but these should be overcome if the conditions above are met. These principles are based on the maximum forces likely to be experienced during normal road use but will not be sufficient to restrain the load when a vehicle is involved in an accident. The recommendations in this Code are therefore not intended to cover an accident situation where greatly increased forces are likely to be encountered.

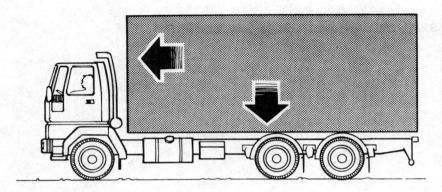

Figure 1

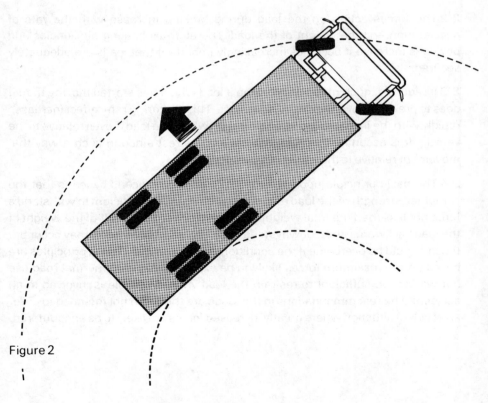

Figure 2

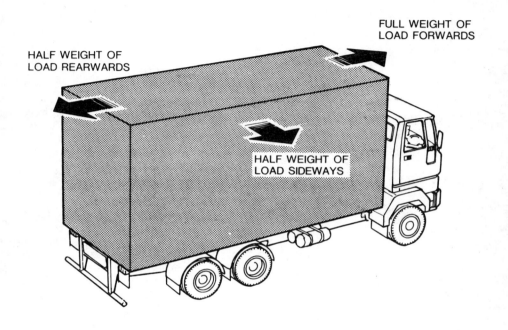

HALF WEIGHT OF
LOAD REARWARDS

FULL WEIGHT OF
LOAD FORWARDS

HALF WEIGHT OF
LOAD SIDEWAYS

Figure 3

SECTION 3. CHOICE OF VEHICLE AND ARRANGEMENT OF LOADS

CHOICE OF VEHICLE

3.1 It is management's responsibility to provide suitable vehicles and securing equipment for each load carried and to ensure that drivers and loading staff are competent and have received sufficient instruction in its use. It is the driver's duty to check and ensure that the load is adequately secured at all times.

3.2 The design and construction of the vehicle and its bodywork should be suitable for the loads which it is likely to carry, particularly in terms of the characteristics and strengths of the materials used. Rotproofing and anti corrosion treatments of load bearing components are highly desirable. When a vehicle is to be carried on a ship, as in roll-on, roll-off, ferry operations provision should be made for the extra load restraint needed and chassis anchorage points to secure the vehicle to the deck.

3.3 The maximum expected load on the floor should be ascertained so that the floor itself and the section and spacing of supporting crossbeams is sufficient. In any calculation account should be taken not only of the load itself but also any extra forces due to the loading method eg the use of fork lift trucks on the floor during loading/unloading.

3.4 The relationship between the vehicle's wheelbase, body length and body overhang should be carefully considered in relation to the composition of the loads to be carried especially if full use is to be made of permitted maximum axle loads.

3.5 The overall height of a loaded vehicle must be checked to ensure that it is less than that of any overhead obstruction likely to be encountered en route. The regulations (see Section 1 paragraph 5) require certain types of vehicle, and others carrying certain loads, to have the maximum height of the vehicle displayed inside the cab so that it is clearly visible to the driver.

3.6 To prevent vehicles grounding on level crossings etc regulations require that a certain minimum ground clearance for trailers must be maintained (see Regulation 74A of the Motor Vehicles (Construction and Use) Regulations 1978, as amended by Amendment No 2 of 1983: SI 1983 No 471). This is particularly important for low loading trailers.

ARRANGEMENT OF LOADS

3.7 Before a vehicle is loaded it should be checked to ensure that its load platform, bodywork, anchorage points or twist locks, as appropriate to the load, are in sound and serviceable condition.

3.8 It is imperative that the maximum permitted axle and gross weight limits are not exceeded. Where part of the load is to be picked up or removed in the course of a journey the effect on axle and gross weights must not be overlooked. Although removal of part of the load will reduce the gross weight the change in weight distribution may cause individual axles to become overloaded.

3.9 Normally the load should be arranged so that it does not obstruct the driver's field of vision including rear view through the driving mirrors. In the case of wide or long projecting loads or where the load obscures obligatory lights, reflectors, rear markings or registration plates care must be taken to comply with the requirements of the Road Vehicles Lighting Regulations 1984–SI 1984 No 812.

3.10 If practicable, the load should be placed in contact with a headboard. Where this is not practicable then additional means of securing must be used. Possible methods include:

a) an obstacle fitted transversely across the vehicle platform and firmly attached to the chassis frame;

b) blocks, scotches or wedges to prevent individual items of a load moving in any direction. Care must be taken to ensure that these are adequately secured to the vehicle platform;

c) additional lashing.

3.11 In order to achieve maximum vehicle stability the load should be placed so that the centre of gravity is kept as low as practicable and near to the vehicle's longitudinal centre line.

This means that where practicable:

a) the load should be spread to give an even weight distribution over the floor area;

b) when a load is stacked the larger and heavier items should be placed at the bottom (see Fig 4);

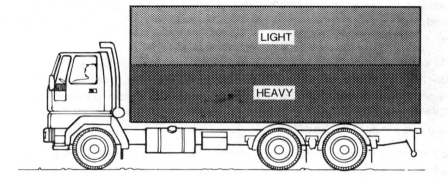

Figure 4

c) the heavier items should be placed nearer to the longitudinal centre line of the vehicle and the lighter ones towards the sides.

3.12 The weight of heavy loads of small dimensions should be distributed across the vehicle platform by the use of load spreading devices.

3.13 Great care must be taken when loading semi-trailers which have no means of support other than the retractable legs. If the front of the trailer is loaded first it is possible for it to 'nose dive'. Trestles or similar supports should be used beneath the fifth wheel coupling plate if it is necessary to work underneath a laden or part laden semi-trailer.

3.14 Before setting off on a journey all tensioners and turn buckles must be adequately tightened and properly stowed. However they must not be over tightened by using levers etc which are longer than those recommended by the manufacturer because this leads to over stressing and possible failure of the lashing or damage to the load.

3.15 The load should be checked frequently for security and the lashings tested for adequate tension after the vehicle has travelled a few miles and again at intervals during the journey. Weather conditions affect the tension of rope lashings and this may lead to damage of the load or loss of security if these are not correctly re-tensioned.

3.16 All loose chains, for example those used for loading skip containers, loose ropes, and other means of lashing, must be properly stowed.

SECTION 4. ANCHORAGE POINTS, HEADBOARDS AND INTERNAL PARTITIONS

ANCHORAGE POINTS

4.1 Traditional rope hooks cannot restrain other than light loads. For this reason it may be necessary to equip some vehicles, particularly those with platform bodies, with additional load anchorage points. These should be designed and integrated into the structure so that the forces imposed on them are transmitted to the main chassis frame of the vehicle.

4.2 *Capacity:* Load anchorage points should be rated at capacities of 0.5 tonne, 1.0 tonne or 2.0 tonne and upwards. The capacity of each anchorage point may not be indicated on the vehicle but the vehicle manufacturer or bodybuilder should provide information on the capacity of each anchorage point. The design and construciton must allow a safety factor of twice the specified capacity acting in any direction through which the lashing can be attached.

4.3 *Design:* No specific recommendations are made about the design of anchorage points but they must be compatible with the type of securing equipment used.

4.4 *Fitting:* Anchorage points should be firmly attached either directly to the chassis or to a metal crosspiece or outrigger. Anchorage points which are secured only to wooden members are unlikely to provide the restraint required. The fitting of additional anchorage points to existing vehicles must in no way weaken the chassis or body structure. In particular, holes must not be drilled in the top or lower flanges of the chassis side members and welding to the chassis without the approval of the original manufacturer is not recommended. Fig 5 illustrates a suggested anchorage point of 2.0 tonne load capacity.

4.5 *Number to be fitted:* Sufficient load anchorage points should be provided in relation to platform length with at least three each side or such greater number as is necessary to ensure that the sum of the capacity of the anchorage points is not less than the maximum rated load of the vehicle. Thus a 3.0 tonne rated load would require at least three per side each of 0.5 tonne capacity. In the case of

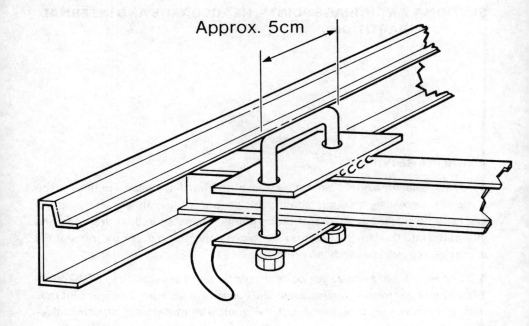

Figure 5

higher rated loads the number of anchorage points and their capacity will also depend on whether the vehicle is purpose built for a particular type of traffic or is to be engaged in general haulage operations where the size and weight of individual items may vary considerably. Thus an operator of a 20 tonne rated load vehicle used exclusively for a particular commodity might need to choose between specifying 40 x 0.5 tonne points, 20 x 1.0 tonne points, or 10 x 2.0 tonne points depending on the character of the load. On the other hand, the general haulier with a similar vehicle used for miscellaneous loads would in all probability need six or more 2.0 tonne points plus enough 1.0 tonne or 0.5 tonne points to make up at least the required 20 tonne of restraint. Here again the precise pattern would depend upon foreknowledge of the types of load to be carried.

4.6 *Number to be used:* The number of anchorage points actually used on a particular journey will depend on the weight and dimensions of the load being carried and its location on the platform in relation to the headboard or other additional means of restraint.

The table below gives some suggested values *but* in some cases additional restraint by the headboard or other means would be required.

1. 2 Axle Vehicles (Flats/Pickups/Drop Sided)

BODY LENGTH		NUMBER OF ANCHORAGE POINTS				
		Minimum 0.5 tonne anchorages				
	PAYLOAD (tonnes)	UP TO 2	2—4	4—6	6—8	8+
MINIMUM	TO 12FT (3.65m)	6	8	10	12	—
12FT	TO 16FT (4.87m)	8	10	12	16	18
16FT	TO 20FT (6.09m)	10	12	14	18	20
20FT	TO 24FT (7.31m)	12	14	16	20	24

2. 3 To 4 Axle Vehicles

		Minimum 0.5 tonne anchorages			
	PAYLOAD (tonnes)	UP TO 10	10—12	12—16	16+
MINIMUM	TO 18FT (5.48m)	14	16	18	20
18FT	TO 24FT	18	20	22	24
24FT	ABOVE	20	22	24	28

FOR VEHICLES CARRYING HEAVY CONCENTRATED LOADS ON A REGULAR BASIS IT IS PREFERABLE TO HAVE WELDED øEYE BOLTS/ SHACKLES LET INTO DECKING/SIDE RAVES AT A JOINED CROSS MEMBER

3. TRAILERS

Trailers should also conform to the above weight/length dimensions for securing lugs.

ø EYE BOLTS TO BS 4278
ø SHACKLES TO BS 3032 and BS 3551
ø STEEL HOOKS TO BS 2903

HEADBOARDS AND FRONT BULKHEADS

4.7 A headboard, when fitted, should be treated as part of the load restraint system since a headboard meeting this Code should be able to restrain half the rated payload of the vehicle in the forward direction. [Some exceptions are listed at the end of this section.]

4.8 *Strength:* A headboard should be capable of withstanding a horizontal force uniformly distributed over its vertical area equal to half the rated payload of the vehicle. IMPORTANT see Section 7 paragraph 1 for factors which reduce effectiveness. The design must be such that the whole body and vehicle structure will withstand the forces imposed on it when the headboard is loaded as described above.

4.9 *Width:* The headboard width should be equal to the width of the loading platform unless the type of load permits a narrower headboard. It should however not be less than the width of the cab.

4.10 *Height:* The headboard height should be sufficient to obstruct forward movement of the type of load which the vehicle is designed to carry unless adequate load restraint is provided by other means.

4.11 The headboard should not have apertures large enough to allow penetration by any part of the load. Large apertures should be covered with a steel mesh or similar material.

4.12 When loads such as metal bars, beams, girders, sheet metal etc are liable to penetrate the cab in the event of failure of the securing devices the headboard must be adequately reinforced to resist damage from individual elements of the load.

4.13 *In Use*

(i) *Loading*

For the maximum benefit to be derived from a headboard it is essential that the

14

load is in contact with it. If a space is left so that the load can move forwards before reaching the headboard then its restraining capacity will be greatly reduced.

(ii) *Damage*

Headboards should be examined frequently for damage. Particular attention should be given to timber panels or boards and to the headboard to chassis mounting points. Damaged headboards should not be used for restraint purposes.

4.14 Bulkheads on small closed vans

In the case of closed vans of 3.5 tonne gross vehicle weight (G.V.W.) or more, where the cab is an integral part of the body, a bulkhead must be fitted, between the load compartment and the cab. Such a bulkhead should afford adequate proteciton to cab personnel and should be designed to resist a uniformly distributed horizontal force of at least 0.5 x the weight of the load.

INTERNAL PARTITIONS

4.15 Vehicles are sometimes divided by internal partitions into a number of compartments each of which is self-sufficient in terms of load restraint. The headboard or internal partition should be designed to resist a uniformly distributed horizontal force of 0.5 x rated load for that compartment.

EXCEPTIONS (see paragraph 4.7)

4.16 Bodies designed specifically for loads which are to be restrained by means other than the headboard. eg refrigerated vans (load should not bear against the reefer unit). These vehicles should carry a manufacturer's plate clearly stating the types of load for which they are intended and the method of load restraint to be used.

4.17 Trestle type headboards or bolsters for supporting long loads. These should carry a manufacturer's plate clearly stating the rated load capacity both vertically and horizontally because the forces will be determined by the type of load carried. eg, a bolster to support a crane jib will not require the same horizontal strength as a bolster to support one end of a steel girder.

4.18 Vehicles used for the carriage of carcass meat. These should be equipped with rails and sliding hooks and be adequately lit. The rails should be fitted with fixed hinged 'stops' at 4—5ft intervals to prevent the surging or sliding of carcases due to motion of the vehicle or brake application

When loading the vehicle the carcasses should be distributed evenly on *all* rails and the stops applied. If part off-loading takes place the remaining load should be re-distributed evenly and the 'stops' re-applied.

4.19 At all times the floor of the vehicle should be kept clear of blood and other slippery matter.

In addition to the load safety methods described in this Code extra provisions are necessary when animals are carried on road vehicles. A list of the main regulations and approved Codes of Practice currently applicable to the carriage of animals is given at Appendix C.

SECTION 5. LOAD SECURING EQUIPMENT

5.1 The selection of the best means of securing a load to a vehicle will depend on the type and composition of the load to be carried. Operators should equip themselves with the correct securing equipment for the types of load carried and where general cargoes are carried various types should be available. Clamps, special bolts, steel wire ropes, chains, webbing harnesses, nets, ropes and shoring bars are all suitable devices for use in load restraint but it is essential to ensure that they are strong enough for the weight of loads carried.

5.2 All equipment used for securing loads should be regularly inspected for wear or damage. Special attention should be paid to webbing and rope to ensure that there is no visible deterioration due to constant use, such as fraying of the strands, and that they have not been cut or damaged in any other way through misuse. If there is any doubt as to whether repairs are required, reference should be made to the manufacturer or suppliers of the lashing.

5.3 Steel wire rope made up into special straps or slings is suitable for securing a load when used in conjunction with other devices such as shackles and thimbles. The strength of steel wire rope will depend on the quality of the steel used, the number of strands, the number of wires in each strand, the diameter of the rope and the method of construction. Wire ropes must have a safe working load compatible with the requirements of the load being carried. Recommendations for the minimum breaking load of various sizes and types of wire rope are contained in BS 302, BS 1290 gives safe working loads for wire rope slings, and BS 6210 is a Code of Practice for wire rope slings. Wire ropes having a diameter of less than 8mm will not be suitable for load restraint purposes. Wire ropes should be free from rust and must not be used if they show evidence of weakening such as broken wires or strands. Other coupling equipment used with wire rope must be of corresponding quality and strength. Sharp bends will reduce the effective strength of wire rope.

5.4 Chains are suitable for lashing loads when used in a similar manner to steel wire ropes. Three properties determine the strength of a chain: the length of its links, the quality of metal used and thickness of the links. A chain with a given link diameter and material will possess varied strengths depending upon the length of the link. The longer the link the more susceptible is the chain to damage–long links can easily be deformed if they are tensioned over a corner. The chain used should be compatible with the requirements of the load carried

Recommendations for the safe working of various sizes of steel chain are contained in BS 6405, BS 1663, BS 4942 and BS 6304. The use of iron or split link chain is not recommended. Chains will be used in conjunction with tensioners and turn buckles which must have a safe working load compatible with that of the chain

5.5 Webbing assemblies are suitable for securing many types of load. They usually consist of a webbing strap with some form of end fittings and incorporate a tensioning device. It is recommended that webbing assemblies manufactured to comply with BS 5759 are used. These will be marked with a Rated Assembly Strength which should never be exceeded. Sleeves and corner protectors should be used to avoid damage to either the load or the webbing where the harness crosses the sharp corners of a load. Care should be taken to ensure that the metal components of the harness do not become corroded or damaged, that the webbing is not cut and that all stitching is sound. Advice should be sought from the manufacturers before repairs are carried out.

5.6 Nets securing or retaining some types of load may be constructed from webbing straps or ropes of either natural or man-made fibres or steel wire. Webbing nets are generally used as barriers to divide the load space into compartments. Rope or cord nets may be used to secure loads either to pallets or direct to the vehicle as the primary restraint system. Lighter nets can be used to cover open bodied vehicles and skips when the type of load makes it unnecessary to use a sheet. It is recommended that nets which comply with BS 6451 should be used. Care should be taken to ensure that the metal components of nets do not become corroded or damaged, that the webbing is not cut and that all stitching is sound. Rope and cord nets should be checked for cuts or other damage to the fibres. If necessary repairs should be carried out by a competent person before the net is used again.

5.7 Rope used for lashings should preferably be manufactured from polypropylene, polyester, sisal or manilla. Polyamide (nylon) ropes are not so suitable as they tend to stretch under load. Ropes should be of 3 strand

18

construction and must have a minimum nominal diameter of at least 10mm. The ends of the rope should be spliced or otherwise treated to prevent fraying. Rope should be selected having regard to the maximum loading to be imposed in each lashing and it is recommended that ropes manufactured to BS 2052 or 4928 should be used. The maximum rated load for these ropes should be indicated by the manufacturer on an attached label or sleeve. Knots and sharp bends will reduce the effective strength of rope and the strength of sisal or manilla rope is also likely to be reduced by water saturation. Wet ropes should always be allowed to dry naturally. When a rope passes over sharp edges of a load some form of corner protector or sleeve should be used to prevent the rope being cut or otherwise damaged.

5.8 Purpose made clamps are suitable for securing loads which are fitted with lifting pockets, brackets or other specially designed attachments. In most cases it will be necessary to reinforce the deck of the vehicle in the vicinity of the clamp position. The design of the clamp and reinforcement should be carried out in accordance with the recommendation of the vehicle manufacturer. A minimum of four clamps should be used and three of these must be strong enough to restrain the load if one clamp fails to function correctly.

5.9 ISO freight containers may be secured to the vehicle by means of special container locks commonly known as twist locks. In most cases twist locks will be fitted to the vehicle during manufacture but where they are fitted at a later date then modifications to the chassis/structure should be carried out in accordance with the recommendations of the vehicle manufacturer. Twist locks should be inspected regularly for wear, damage and correct operation. Locking devices, which are intended to prevent the operating levers from moving during transit, should be given special attention. A minimum of four twist locks should be provided for each container carried.

5.10 For use of sheets see Section 6 paragraphs 11—13 and Section 7 paragraphs 8 and 11.

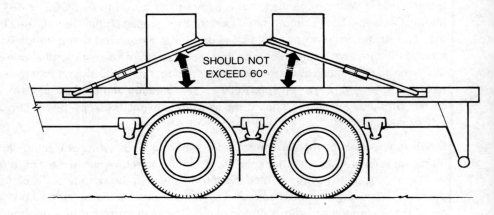

SHOULD NOT
EXCEED 60°

Figure 6

20

SECTION 6. GENERAL REQUIREMENTS FOR SECURING LOADS

6.1 The total load restraint system will generally consist of a combination of:

a) lashings secured to anchorage points attached to the vehicle chassis which includes cross bearers, outriggers etc;

b) baulking arrangements including headboards, bulkheads, spigots, transverse beams, shoring bars etc which are securely attached to the vehicle;

c) friction between the load and the vehicle platform.

In most circumstances it would be appropriate to obtain the majority of the total restraint required from (a), and the remaining part from (b). Benefits accrued from (c) should be regarded as a bonus. Vehicles using fabric sides, for example curtain siders, normally still require additional internal restraints.

6.2 The restraining system should be so arranged that failure or slackening of a single component does not render the remainder of the system ineffective.

6.3 The securing system should be so arranged that no part can be accidentally released by vibration or road shocks while the vehicle is in motion.

6.4 Headboards, sideboards and tailboards fitted to vehicles, if adequately constructed, may provide some restraint to movement of the load. Light loads may be carried on this type of vehicle without additional restraint provided that the height of the load is less than the height of the boards, and that there is no risk of the load moving and breaking through any of the boards. In any instance where the load exceeds the height of any of the boards some form of lashing must be used.

6.5 On platform vehicles some form of load restraining device will always be required.

6.6 All items of loose equipment not in use (sheets, ropes, dunnage etc) and loose surplus equipment in service (rope ends etc) must be securely restrained at all times and wherever they are placed.

6.7 In order to obtain the maximum efficiency from every part of the restraint system it is essential that the requirements described in the following paragraphs are met.

A. Lashings

6.8 The lashings and fastening devices (ropes, webbings, chains, cables, clamps etc) should be in sound condition and must be capable of withstanding all normal forces. To avoid movement of the load, lashings must be properly tensioned at all times using a tensioning device specified by the manufacturer of the lashing. Never overtension lashings by the use of levers.

6.9 It is most important that lashings which provide forward restraint are as near to the horizontal as possible and never at an angle of more than 60°, because the loading increases sharply as the lashings approach the vertical position (see Fig 6).

6.10 Lashings should be protected against abrasion and/or cutting by the use of corner protectors or protective sleeves.

B. Sheets

6.11 Except in the case of very light bulk loads conventional sheets (tarpaulins) should be regarded as providing no more than weather protection and the load must be independently secured. However, purpose made load sheets embodying webbing straps are available (see Fig 7) and are satisfactory up to their rated load capacity   rovided the straps are secured to body attachments of equivalent strength.

6.12 Where more than one sheet is needed to cover a load the rearmost one should be put on first and then the following ones put on working progressively towards the front of the vehicle (see Figs 8—10). This will ensure that the overlapping part of the sheets faces rearwards so preventing the penetration of wind, driving rain, snow and sleet. The same principle should be applied to folds at the front or on the sides of the vehicle so that wind pressure will tend to close any gaps or folds in the sheet. There should be no loose flaps or tears in the sheet which might cause danger to other road users when the vehicle is moving (see Fig 11). Care should be taken to avoid striking passers-by when throwing lashings over loads during the securing operation.

6.13 After the sheeting and roping is completed ensure that all loose rope ends have been tied up and that the lights, reflectors, number plates and rear markings etc have not been obscured by any part of the sheet.

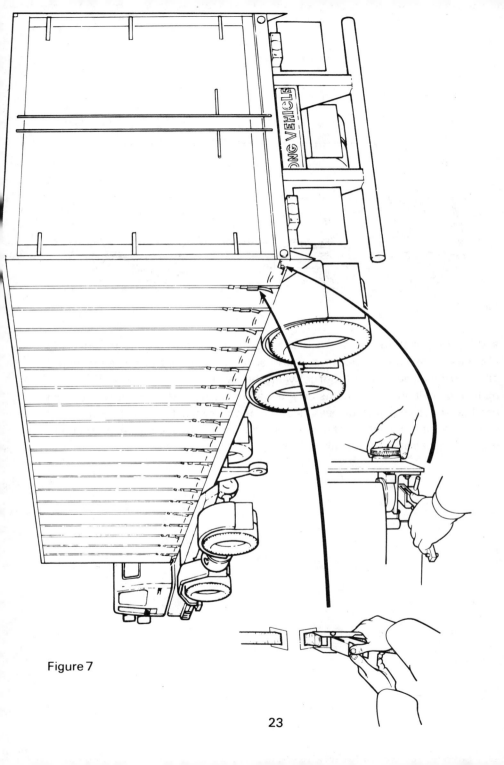

Figure 7

23

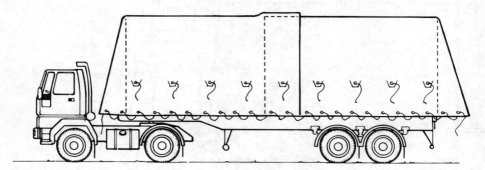

Figure 8

a) Where more than one sheet is required to cover and protect the load the rearmost sheet is positioned first. This ensures that overlaps do not face forward allowing wind and rain etc to get between sheets.

b) Having positioned the sheets on the load ensuring that all parts are covered and that sheets are equal on each side, secure the front of the rear sheet followed by the rear of the front sheet. Do not overtighten or sheets will be drawn up to expose the load at the rear or at the front.

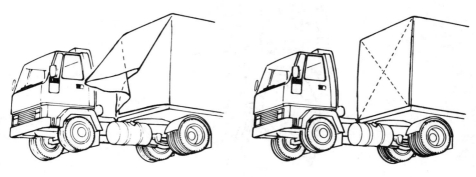

Figure 9

c) The next stage is to secure the front of the sheet.
1. Step 1. Draw in surplus sheet from sides, cross over front and secure.
   Step 2. Draw down over cross-overs the remaining surplus sheet to form a full width flat front flap.

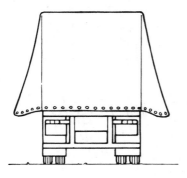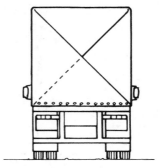

Figure 10

d) Having secured front sheet, secure the sides of the rear sheet to the rearmost corners.
e) Rear of the load should be sheeted and folded as illustrated above (right).

25

Figure 11

C. Nets

6.14 Nets and their attachments (lashing ropes, border ropes, hooks etc) should be in sound condition.

6.15 The maximum rated loading of the net should never be exceeded.

6.16 Nets must be properly tensioned using a tensioning device specified by the net manufacturer. Never overtension a net by the use of a lever or other unauthorised device.

6.17 The mesh size should always be less than the smallest item the net is expected to retain; except that this will not always apply to nets used to retain loose bulkloads because these are not subject to the same loading conditions.

6.18 Protection against abrasion and/or cutting should be provided by the use of corner protectors or corner sleeves.

D. Baulking

6.19 Chocks, wedges and scotches may be used to prevent individual items of a load from moving in any horizontal direction. Care must be taken to ensure that these are stout enough and are adequately secured to the vehicle platform.

E. Dunnage

6.20 It is preferable for all the individual units or packages comprising a load to be packed closely together before any restraint lashings are applied. If this is not possible then some form of packing, commonly known as dunnage, must be used to fill any gaps which exist between parts of the load or between the load and the vehicle sides.

6.21 The use of loose dunnage between the load and the platform should be avoided wherever possible but where it must be used to support an awkwardly shaped load it should be secured so as to prevent movement during the journey.

6.22 Care must be taken not to damage the load by using unsuitable dunnage and therefore the choice of material will be governed to some extent by the type of load being carried. A number of materials are suitable for use as dunnage, the most common being timber, folded cardboard, hardboard, high density foam, and air bags. Timber dunnage should be of uniform thickness and maximum possible width. The minimum width should, where practicable, be twice the thickness and it is always preferable to use only a single layer.

F. Friction

6.23 A slippery platform surface is always dangerous and the aim should be to obtain the maximum advantage from the frictional restraint by keeping both the base of the load and the platform surface as clean, dry and free from grease as possible.

G. Load Anchorage Points

6.24 Lashings used to restrain the load must always be attached to anchorage points which have sufficient strength to absorb the expected loading. Always remember that any restraint system is only as strong as its *weakest* component.

6.25 Anchorage points should themselves be firmly attached either directly to the chassis or to a metal crosspiece or outrigger.

6.26 Anchorage points which are secured to wooden members only are not likely to be strong enough to provide the restraint required.

6.27 Rope hooks should only be used for roping, and then only for relatively light loads. They should not be used in place of the proper anchorage points.

6.28 The rated load capacity of the anchorage point must never be exceeded.

SECTION 7. GENERAL FREIGHT

7.1 The loading and securing of general freight loads on goods vehicles is difficult due to the wide diversity of shape, size and nature of this type of load. Vehicles equipped with headboards, tailboards or sideboards, or van bodies, will provide some restraint to movement of the load. However, additional load restraining devices will be required under the following conditions:

a) If there is a risk that the load may break through the walls, sideboards or tailboard of the vehicle;

b) When the load is higher than the headboard, sideboard or tailboard of the vehicle;

c) If the load is liable to be damaged should it move during transit.

7.2 When general freight loads are carried on platform vehicles some form of load restraining device will always be required.

LOADING ARRANGEMENT ON VEHICLE

7.3 Two essential requirements must be satisfied when loading vehicles. These are that the load must be so distributed that

a) the maximum permitted gross vehicle weight and axle weights are not exceeded, and

b) maximum stability is ensured when the vehicle is braked, or accelerated or changes direction.

7.4 For maximum stability the items comprising the total load are required to be evenly spread to achieve minimum height and to be so arranged as to form a unified whole so that no excessive stress is applied to whatever restraining devices are used. Where a part of the load is to be picked up or removed in the course of a journey the effect on gross vehicle weight, individual axle weights and on the securing and stability of the load then being carried must not be

29

overlooked. Although removal of part of the load will reduce the gross vehicle weight, it may so change the weight distribution as to cause individual axles to exceed their plated weight and this possibility must be borne in mind during the initial loading operation.

7.5 In addition to the general principles outlined above the following procedures should be followed whenever applicable:

a) Where mixed loads involve heavy solid articles and light crushable boxes etc, the former should provide the base and rear part ('A' in Fig 12) and the light portion to be loaded on top and to the front ('B' in Fig 12).

b) Throughout the journey, the load should frequently be checked for security and the lashings tested for adequate tension after the vehicle has travelled a few miles and again at intervals during the journey. Weather conditions can effect the tension of ropes and this may lead to damage of the load or loss of security if these are not correctly re-tensioned.

c) Where mixed goods involve different sizes of container, small items should be central, with the larger items forming the outer walls of the load. Avoid as far as possible obstructions or projections beyond the vehicle sides (see Fig 13).

d) Keep irregular shaped items for the upper part of the load where it is not possible to place them centrally within the load.

e) The load must be packed tightly before applying restraint.

f) Special precautions may have to be taken when dangerous substances are included in a load, eg segregation of substances which may interact together; protection from rain; careful handling and stowage to reduce the risk of damage to vulnerable containers (see Section 1 paragraph 4).

RESTRAINT DEVICES

7.6 A variety of materials may be used for restraining general freight loads. These include rope chains, steel wire rope, webbing, strapping or net. For the securing of loads inside van bodies and similar load containers, specially designed shoring poles used in conjunction with the appropriate securing fixtures on the vehicle deck and sides are suitable. Purpose built restraining devices should only be used for application and in the manner approved by their respective manufacturers.

7.7 The selection and use of restraining devices should be based on the principles contained in Section 5 of this Code. However, there are some special points which need to be considered when dealing with general freight and these are outlined in the following paragraphs.

7.8 Sheets may be used subject to the conditions outlined in Section 6 paragraphs 11—13 of this Code. Where several sheets are required to cover one load they should be put on at the rear of the load first (see Figs 8—10). This ensures the overlapping portions of the sheets face rearwards so preventing wind, driving rain, snow and sleet penetrating between them. The same principle must be applied to folds in the sheets at the front or on the sides of the vehicle–so that wind pressure will tend to close any gaps or folds in the sheet. After being sheeted and roped a vehicle should present a neat, compact and safe picture–not only when the vehicle is stationary but also on the move. The following points should always be checked:

a) The lights, reflectors, number plates and rear markings etc should not be obscured;

b) All loose rope ends should be tied up;

c) There should be no loose flaps or tears in the sheet liable to cause danger to other road users when the vehicle is moving (see Fig 11).

LOADING METHODS

7.9 In view of the wide diversity of general loads it is not possible to suggest loading methods for all the types of loads likely to be encountered. However the basic precautions outlined in Section 6 of this Code will always be applicable. Loading methods for certain general categories of loads are outlined in the following paragraphs.

7.10 Rolls, Drums or Cylindrical Loads

a) Rolls or cylindrical items should ideally be placed with their axis across the vehicle in order that the rolling tendency will be to the front or rear. Use chocks and lashings liberally to secure them. Fig 14 illustrates a load consisting of paper or cardboard rolls. When the bottom layer of rolls has been positioned and secured on the platform and the first roll of the second layer ('A' in Fig 14) loaded, the overlashings are laid over 'A' and across the top of the remaining bottom layer rolls. No tension is applied to the lashings at this stage. The remaining rolls in the second layer are now loaded and at the conclusion the 'between-layers' lashings are secured to the rear of the vehicle and 'top-over' lashings applied if required. A tarpaulin sheet is normally added to assist with lateral restraint and to give weather protecton (see Fig 15). 'Between-layers' lashings, as illustrated, may be omitted when metal or concrete pipes are carried, since the weight and abrasive nature of the load would excessively damage the lashings.

31

Only the top lashings are retained but liberal use of chocks is essential. The use of fore and aft lashings between layers provides extra security on acceleration and braking whilst also providing some side-thrust-resistance from lashings 'biting' into rolls. NB. these particular lashings may have to be omitted if the customer so dictates or if the 'biting' damages the load. The omission should be made good by extra top lashings and chocks and cradles.

b) If the length of the cylinders is less than twice their diameter they should be placed on end unless instructions are given to the contrary by the consignor. If the length is greater than twice the diameter, but less than the width of the vehicle, they must be positioned so as to roll forwards. Each row must contact the one in front, and rear ones must be chocked to prevent rolling backwards or forwards.

c) If the drums, rolls etc are standing on end, lashings must be used to prevent lateral movement and further cross lashings must be applied. If on their sides, they should have at least one cross lashing for each item. If there is more than one layer the rearmost roll must be restrained by lashing or blocking against rearward motion.

7.11 Boxes. Boxes must be loaded so that they are prevented from moving in any direction. They must interlock if possible, and be loaded to a uniform height. Heavier boxes should be at the bottom of the load. There must be at least one lashing for each row of boxes across the vehicle and any sheeting employed must be considered supplementary to the primary load restraint system. Any box which is above the general height of the load must have at least one cross lashing, and more depending on weight and size.

7.12 Sacks.

a) When possible sacks should be laid on their sides with alternate layers in opposite directions. In any event no more than two successive layers should be in the same direction. The load should be of uniform height when possible.

b) There must be at least one cross lashing for each sack length. Loads of sacks should be sheeted if possible.

c) With certain loads the use of tensioners may be desirable. This is particularly true of loads which tend to settle around the lashings.

d) Empty sacks, which can fall from a vehicle when in motion, can be extremely hazardous and these must therefore be securely restrained to the vehicle's platform.

7.13 Sheet Glass. This type of load should normally be carried on purpose built vehicles embodying specially designed glass clamps and supports. However, when sheet or plate glass is carried in crates or on timber pallets load restraint precautions as for general freight apply.

7.14 Loose Bricks. Loose brick restraining systems must restrain both the bulk mass of the load and individual bricks. These requirements can be met by load-surrounding sides, bulkhead and tailboard all of which satisfy requirements given in Section 4. The load height should not exceed the height of the surrounding body. Purpose-made restraint systems may also be used for securing this type of load providing the strength of both these and the load securing points used is equal to the load being restrained. Sheeting should only be used subject to the conditions given in Section 6.

7.15 Mixed Loads. When a load is composed of different items each part of the load must be secured in a manner suitable to a load of its type. This applies mainly to cross lashings. The longitudinal lashings must be adequate for the total weight of the load, and separators must be used so that no part of the load can move forward independently.

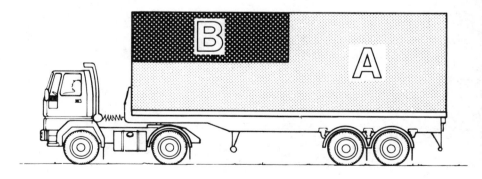

Figure 12

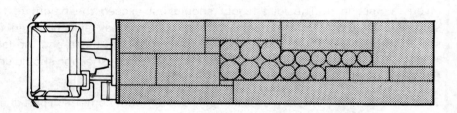

Figure 13

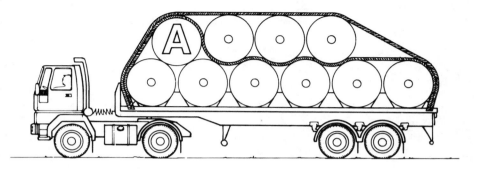

Figure 14

A tarpaulin sheet is normally added to assist with lateral restraint and give weather protection see Figure 15.

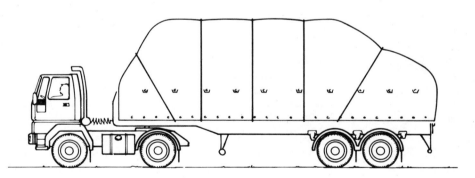

Figure 15

SECTION 8. METAL LOADS

GENERAL

8.1 Small relatively heavy items, such as small castings, if not palletised, should be carried on sided vehicles. The headboard, sideboards, and tailboard must be higher than the load and must be strong enough to withstand the forces generated by the vehicle's motion.

8.2 Careful attention should be paid to points where lashings pass over corners of the load to ensure that the load is not damaged by chain links etc nor that the lashings are damaged by sharp edges. Corner protectors should be used whenever necessary.

8.3 The friction between individual items in a load will generally be low, particularly if the metal is oiled, and should therefore be disregarded when assessing the total load restraint required. The friction between load and vehicle platform will also be considerably reduced if either is wet or greasy.

8.4 A large mass is less likely to move about on a vehicle platform than a number of small items and therefore whenever possible loads should be aggregated into the largest or heaviest unit feasible. This will be controlled to some extent by the facilities available at the point of unloading.

8.5 Banding (steel or plastic), commonly used for binding loads together, is not an adequate method for securing loads to vehicles. The wide range of banding available makes it difficult to ensure that the type to be used has sufficient strength for the task and there is a real risk that it will work loose during the journey. If this happens the driver has no means of re-tightening it.

8.6 Metal loads can take various forms but they can be broadly divided into 6 categories:

    a) flat sheet

    b) long sections

c) coils

d) large units and castings

e) scrap metal

f) scrap vehicles.

FLAT SHEET

8.7 When mixed sizes of sheet or plate are being carried the smallest should normally be loaded on top and at the front of the vehicle so that they cannot slide forward.

8.8 Oiled flat sheet should be bundled and packed in steel sheets which form a box around the bundle, commonly known as trumpeting.

8.9 It is essential that the lashings are always in firm contact with the top surface of the load. If the load is level with, or lower than, the side raves of the vehicle then the lashings are likely to be ineffective. In these instances the load should be raised off the floor by the use of timber packing.

8.10 Flat sheet is sometimes loaded onto pallets in which case the advice given in Section 11 should also be followed.

LONG SECTIONS

8.11 This type of load will generally be carried along the length of the vehicle and can pose particular problems since one item can easily penetrate a headboard or driver's cab if it is allowed to move. It is essential therefore that the vehicle is loaded in such a way that the complete load forms a unit and no single item can move independently.

8.12 The load will always need to be restrained by lashings, preferably chains or webbings. If possible these should be attached to the vehicle by means of load anchorage points as described in Section 5. When the vehicle is not fitted with such anchorage points it is common practice to pass the lashings around the vehicle to form a continuous loop which is not physically attached to the vehicle in any way. If this method is used the utmost care should be taken to avoid damage to the chassis frame or other vehicle components. A minimum of 4 lashings must be used. It is essential to realise that, although this form of lashing might provide reasonable sideways restraint, forward restraint is provided only by friction and this may be inadequate to restrain the load during heavy braking and some additional means of forward restraint may be necessary. Because there is no 'give' in metal products it will often be an advantage to place a piece of timber at a convenient point between the lashings and the load. This will allow a greater tension to be applied to the lashing.

8.13 If the load is stacked it should be kept as low as possible with the heavier items at the bottom and the lighter ones on top. No layer should be bigger than the one underneath it.

8.14 To prevent forward movement the load should be placed in contact with a headboard or otherwise be securely restrained. To achieve an even weight distribution long loads are sometimes carried on a bolster type headboard so that the load projects forward over the driver's cab. In this case individual items should be aggregated into the largest or heaviest unit feasible and forward restraint provided by lashing the entire load securely to the bolster. Additional restraints will need to be provided at the rear.

8.15 If stanchions, either attached to the vehicle or to specially made bolsters, are used to prevent sideways movement they should extend to the height of the load. Sideboards should not be relied upon to provide more than a minimum of sideways restraint.

COILS

8.16 To avoid confusion over terminology, in the following paragraphs a coil with its hollow centre or bore horizontal is referred to as 'bore horizontal' and a coil with its hollow centre or bore vertical as 'bore vertical'. A coil may be either a single coil or a number of coils bound together with the bores in line so as to form a cylindrical unit.

8.17 Before loading, the coil banding and packaging should be examined to ensure that it is intact and not likely to break apart whilst eg in transit. When banding is used to strap coils and pallets together it is important to appreciate that the banding is intended only to secure the pallet to the coil. Therefore it will usually be necessary to secure the entire unit to the vehicle. Securing the pallet alone is unlikely to be sufficient.

Coils of Wide Sheet-Bore Horizontal

8.18 These coils, when loaded bore horizontal, will preferably be carried on vehicles having a coil well built into the load platform. If there is a likelihood of the coils moving in the well then lashings should be used as necessary. Alternatively coils may, when specialised vehicles are not available for instance, be carried packed on cradles similar in construction to that shown in Fig 16 subject to the conditions laid down in the following paragraphs.

8.19 The coils must be securely attached to the cradle by at least two webbing lashings or by an approved steel strapping. The lashings must be in contact with the surface of the coil and the softwood wedges.

8.20 Coil and cradle units may be carried in rows on the vehicle platform but all coils in a row should be of approximately equal height and contact the row in front or a timber spacer.

8.21 If a coil well is not used, coils or coil and cradle units should be secured to the vehicle by chain or webbing lashings which incorporate tensioning devices. For securing purposes each line of coils across the vehicle is considered separately and each one must be lashed.

8.22 Cradles should not be loaded over coil wells unless a well cover is used having adequate strength to support the weight of the coil.

Coils of Wide Sheet–Bore Vertical

8.23 Coils carried bore vertical are usually loaded onto platform vehicles and are one of the most difficult loads to secure. Figure 17 shows a suitable restraint system employing a cruciform which can be used with chains or webbing to secure the larger diameter coils loaded bore vertical. The coil is placed on the centre line of the vehicle and the cruciform placed on top of the coil with the spigots located inside the bore. The cruciform should be positioned with the open through channel across the line of the vehicle to accommodate a conventional securing chain lashing. Lashings should be attached to the vehicle anchorage points and tensioned in the usual way.

8.24 It is possible to secure such coils without using the clamp described, but great care must be exercised in positioning the webbing or chains to ensure they are fully capable of preventing movement (see Fig 18). Normally it will be necessary to provide heavy duty floor anchorages and to ensure that adequate tensioning methods are available.

8.25 Lighter coils are sometimes packed onto pallets. These should be treated in a similar way to coils packed on cradles and the advice given in paragraphs 17—21 of this Section should be followed.

Coiled Rod and Bar

8.26 These products should be carried bore horizontal in a single layer loaded either transversely or longitudinally on the vehicle platform. Unless the vehicle is

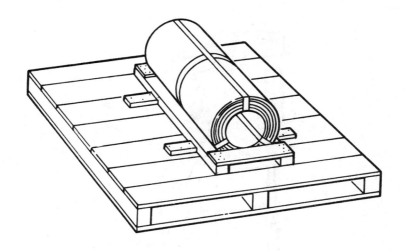

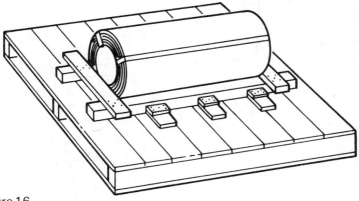

Figure 16

41

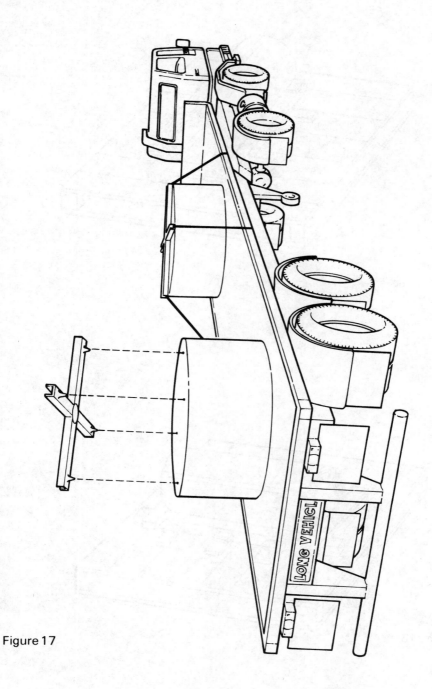

Figure 17

42

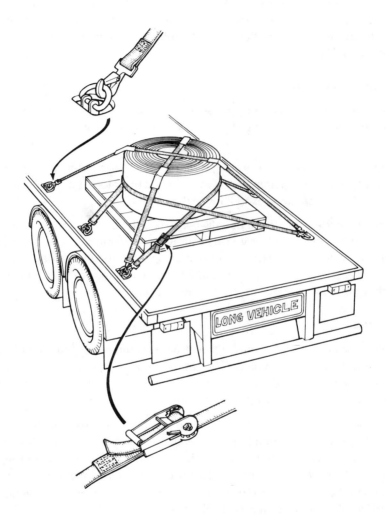

Figure 18

fitted with special loading frames or cradles designed to contain the coils all the sideways restraint will have to be provided by the lashings, preferably chain or webbings fitted with tensioning devices. One method of carrying these coils longitudinaly between parallel rows of timber is described at the end of this Section–paragraphs 35—37.

Large Units and Castings

8.27 These loads are normally carried in a purpose built cradle which must be sufficiently strong to withstand the forces likely to be imposed on it during transportation.

8.28 To achieve a satisfactory weight distribution it will often be impossible to place this type of load against the headboard and therefore it will be necessary to use securely fixed baulking in addition to the lashing.

8.29 Because these loads are usually fairly high the lashings must be arranged to prevent the load toppling as well as to prevent movement on the load platform. Therefore it will be necessary either to lash over the top of the load or to points high on the cradle or load, even though baulking and lashings are used at platform level to provide the majority of the restraint.

Scrap Metal

8.30 Scrap metal can take many forms from machine swarf to motor vehicles. Some loads may come into one of the categories already covered in this Section in which case the loading and securing arrangements should follow the guidance given in that particular sub-section.

8.31 Loose items of scrap may be carried in sided vehicles with no additional means of restraint, provided that the headboard, sideboards, and tailboard are higher than the load. It may be an offence under the Construction and Use Regulations to allow any part of a load to fall or be blown from a vehicle. Therefore it will usually be necessary to cover the load with a sheet or net. Further advice on the carriage of loose bulk loads is given in Section 10.

Scrap Vehicles

8.32 Scrap vehicles are likely to be difficult to transport safely on platform vehicles because the tyres and suspension will permit the load to move making it inherently unstable. Chain or webbing lashings which incorporate tensioning devices should be used to secure these loads.

8.33 Scrap vehicles should not be stacked on each other because it will be almost impossible to position and adequately secure the upper layers in such a way that movement is prevented whilst braking or cornering.

8.34 The practice of securing derelict motor vehicles by means of a lorry mounted crane exerting pressure on the roof of the uppermost vehicle is not considered to provide adequate load security because this method relies upon friction for most of the restraint and failure of a single part of the restraint system, eg the crane, will immediately lead to the load becoming insecure. Further advice on the satisfactory methods of securing motor vehicles to platform bodies is given in Section 14.

One Method of Securing Coiled Rod and Bar

8.35 A recommended method of carrying coiled rod and bar is shown in Fig 19. The principle of this system is to form the coils into a tube parallel to the length of the vehicle, retention equipment being applied to the rear end to hold the front end firmly against a stack of coils bore vertical that are against the vehicle headboard.

8.36 Either one or more rows of coils may be carried depending upon the size and weight of each coil. All of the coils in each row must be of approximately equal diameter.

8.37 The loading is commenced by placing a stack of coils bore vertical onto the double rows of timber at the front of the load platform and in contact with the headboard. The remaining coils are then stacked bore horizontal between the rows of timber leaning against the vertical stack at the front. The coils should be inclined at an angle of approximately 70 degrees to the horizontal. The coils are restrained by placing one end of a short length of stout timber into the bore of the rearmost coils with the other end in contact with the load platform. This piece of timber is then held rigidly against the coil and load platform by a tensionable webbing or chain lashing which is attached to anchorage points slightly forward of the point where the lashing crosses the piece of timber.

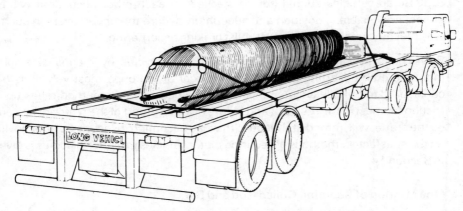

Figure 19   A tarpaulin sheet may be added to give weather protection–see Figure 20.

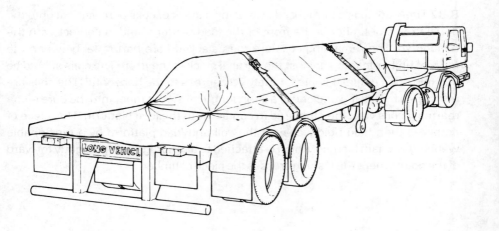

Figure 20

SECTION 9. TIMBER LOADS

9.1 This section is intended to provide general guidance on the measures necessary for the safe carriage of timber, both bulk and sawn. Timber is a 'live' commodity which can lead to independent movement of parts of the load if the restraint is inadequate. It is essential that timber is not loaded to a height, or in such a way, as to result in the likelihood of either the vehicle or load becoming unstable.

SAWN TIMBER

9.2 It is important to ensure that, wherever practicable, the load is placed against the headboard or similar fixed restraint. If this is not possible then all the restraint will have to be provided by the lashings.

9.3 Bulk packaged sheets of timber such as plywood, chip-board etc are generally strapped or wired at each end and before loading the straps should be checked for security. If the straps are damaged or insecure extra care must be taken to ensure that the complete load is adequately secured to the vehicle.

9.4 Loose timber is generally made up into standard sets which should be loaded to a uniform height on the vehicle. The uneven ends should where possible be at the rear of the vehicle and packed out to prevent whip. Generally the use of dunnage should be as outlined in Section 6 paragraphs 20—22.

9.5 Light loads of timber, eg for retail deliveries, can be carried on sided vehicles where the height of the load does not exceed the height of the headboard, sides or tailboard, thus avoiding the need for constant lashing and relashing of the load. Where the height of the load exceeds the height of either the headboard, sides or tailboard, lashings must be used.

Restraining Devices

9.6 In general the use of chain or webbing lashings is recommended. The number of lashings required should be in accordance with the weight of the load and the number of anchorage points used. At least one intermediate lashing should be passed around the lower half of the load only. Care must be taken to ensure that restraining chains or webbing are placed at points where the load is rigid, ie where there are no uneven ends of timber, and that the load is protected from damage by toggles or load binders.

9.7 All types of lashings should be checked regularly because they may need to be retightened several times during the course of the journey as the timber settles on the vehicle, particularly in the early stages of the journey.

9.8 Any loose ends of timber at the rear of the vehicle should also be secured with rope or webbing to minimise whip.

9.9 Certain types of timber loads present a particular problem since the outside lifts and tends to spread sideways, causing the load to belly outwards. To avoid this the vehicle should be fitted with side stanchions that reach the height of the load (see Fig 21). It is essential that the stanchions are capable of resisting any outward movement of the load.

ROUND TIMBER

9.10 In general the principles of load distribution outlined in Section 3 should be adhered to and again it is important to ensure that, whenever possible, the load is placed against the headboard or similar fixed restraint. The use of chain or webbing lashings is recommended and all lashing should be capable of being tightened by use of a toggle or load binder. The lashings should be attached to suitable anchorage points and should be regularly checked during the journey and retightened if necessary.

Stacks on the longitudinal axis

9.11 Each outer log or piece of timber shall be supported by at least two uprights Pieces shorter than the distance between two uprights should be placed in the interior of the load. The uprights should be fitted with top chains, so as to be capable of resisting the load's outward movement. Where a pile is supported by only two pairs of uprights, the ends of the outer logs should extend at least 300mm (12 inches) beyond the uprights where practicable. Logs should preferably be laid top to tail alternatively so as to ensure an even balance of the

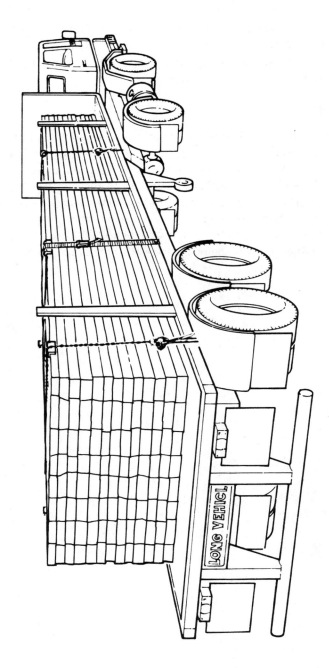

Figure 21

49

load. Each pile should be lashed together and the lashing secured by a suitable device. Where necessary, staples may be used in conjunction with chains. A single chain stretched between uprights, even if well secured, is not enough. For barked roundwood at least two lashings are required.

WHOLE TREES

9.12 The carriage of whole trees is a highly specialised field of timber haulage that is generally accomplished using pole vehicles or vehicles where the timber load is secured to a trailing dolly at one end. Vehicles should be fitted with bolsters and stanchions of sufficient strength to restrain the load. Chains or webbing lashings are necessary for securing the load and generally a minimum of 3 chains or webbing lashings should be used, one of which should bind together any overhanging tails or the middle of an awkwardly shaped load. The lashings should be capable of being tightened using a toggle or load binder.

SECTION 10. LOOSE BULK LOADS

10.1 Loose bulk loads can be described generally as those which do not readily lend themselves to any form of packaging such as sand, ballast, aggregate etc and for ease of loading they are usually carried in open bodied vehicles. Removable open topped containers, commonly known as skips and which are normally used for transporting waste materials, also come into this load category.

10.2 Clearly the loading and securing of such loads do not pose some of the problems associated with other types of load but nevertheless they do present problems peculiar to themselves. Particular attention should be paid to granular or flaked materials which may settle in transit.

10.3 Shedding of loose bulk loads is more likely to take the form of small quantities of material either falling through gaps in the bodywork or being blown from the top of the load compartment.

10.4 The load compartment should be kept in good condition to minimise the risk of leakage. Special attention should be given to drop sides and tailboards where damage or distortion can easily lead to loss of part of the load through any small gaps which are created.

10.5 All the body to chassis attachment points and body fittings such as hinge pins and brackets, tailboard locking mechanisms, drop side fasteners, etc should be secure and in sound condition.

10.6 The body sides should be of sufficient height not only to completely contain the material when it is loaded but also to reduce the likelihood of any part of the load, which might have moved during the journey, from falling or being blown over the edge.

10.7 Body height extensions should only be used where conditions and type of load permit. Where these are used their supports must be adequately fixed to the existing body. It is not considered adequate to rely upon the load within the parent body of the vehicle for support. Where necessary tie chains should be used transversely at the top of body extensions to prevent sideways spread.

10.8 To reduce the risk of part of the load falling or being blown off the top of the load compartment it will usually be necessary to use some form of cover. The necessity for a cover and the type to be used will depend on the nature of the load being carried. Materials such as dry sand and ash, metal turning swarf etc should be covered by a sheet to prevent them from being blown off by wind action. Loads which consist of large items such as scrap metal and builders' waste etc can sometimes be adequately retained by covering with a net.

10.9 Skip containers, when loaded onto the carrying vehicle, must be adequately secured against movement when subjected to braking and cornering forces (see Section 2). Loading chains must be properly stowed.

10.10 Special problems are likely to be encountered with skip containers because the driver does not usually have any control over the packing. However, when the skip container is accepted for loading onto the vehicle the driver must assume responsibility for the safe carriage of the skip and its contents. Therefore the general guidance given in this Section on loads carried in open bodied load compartments should be followed. A sheet or net will usually be needed to prevent the contents from spilling onto the road.

SECTION 11. PALLETS

11.1 The safe carriage of pallets often represents a two fold problem. First there has to be considered the stability of the items stacked on the pallet and secondly the restraint of the pallet and its cargo on the vehicle platform. In the case of small containers and cased machinery, usually only the second factor need be considered. When banding or other similar means are used to unitise a pallet and its cargo it is most important to appreciate that the banding etc is intended only to secure the pallet to its cargo and not the cargo to the pallet. Therefore it will usually be necessary to secure the entire unit to the vehicle. Securing the pallet alone is unlikely to be sufficient.

11.2 There are two basic types of pallet: those which have a number of horizontal bottom members in contact with the vehicle platform and those supported by corner legs and feet. Pallets themselves serve a double purpose in that they enable goods of similar nature and size to be made up into unit loads and also palletised loads can be more easily handled mechanically which reduces the effort required to handle and transport them. Because of the wide variation in the weight and sizes of pallets, situations will arise when the vehicle load space cannot be fully utilised without either exceeding the permitted gross weight or the axle weights. This free load space will increase the likelihood of pallets, which are not properly restrained, moving when the vehicle is braking or cornering.

11.3 Before loading, the pallets should be examined for damage or other obvious signs of weakness. If there is reason to suspect that the pallets are not of sufficient strength to withstnd the load carried on them they should not be accepted for loading.

11.4 Where pallets are carried on vehicles with van bodies, lashings will be required to restrain the pallets if there are spaces between them or between the pallets and the vehicle sides or headboard. This is because, if there is space for the pallet to move, they could develop sufficient momentum to break through the sides or headboard when the vehicle is braking or cornering. Where, for practical reasons, lashings cannot be used then the spaces must be filled with suitable dunnage to prevent movement of the pallets.

11.5 In order to utilise the full payload capacity of the vehicle it may be feasible to stack palletised loads. However the upper layers of pallets must be positioned so that they are stable and adequately secured to prevent them from falling from the vehicle. Unless the upper pallet is directly supported by the lower one, the cargo on the lower pallets must be of sufficient structural strength to withstand the weight of the upper pallet without becoming distorted.

11.6 Individual items in the load must be firmly secured to the pallet if they are not to be dislodged when the vehicle is in motion. Movement of the cargo on the pallet may lead to a failure of the restraint system attached to that pallet and those adjacent to it. Bagged items tend to settle under vibration to fill air spaces between the bags, thus loosening any strapping.

11.7 The following provisions apply to the movement of all types of palletised loads:

(i) The arrangement of the pallets on the vehicle must be such that the maximum permitted gross vehicle weight and axle weights are not exceeded.

(ii) Unless the pallets are adequately constrained by the body or sideboards and headboard of the vehicle, additional means of restraining the horizontal and vertical movement of the pallet should be provided.

(iii) The pallets should be positioned so that the load is balanced across the vehicle.

(iv) Where the load space is not fully utilised and where weight distribution is a problem, pallets should if possible be placed along the longitudinal centre line of the vehicle and 'Closed Up' to one another.

(v) Where pallets are stacked on open platform vehicles restraining lashings or nets must be used to prevent movement of each layer of pallets carried. Tarpaulin sheets and covers are not by themselves adequate for this purpose.

(vi) Where pallets are loaded onto vehicles which have been equipped with a roller loading system extra care should be taken to ensure that the pallets are adequately restrained.

(vii) When part of the load is removed from the vehicle care must be taken that the remaining pallets do not cause the vehicles maximum axle weight to be exceeded or its lateral stability to be impaired.

Restraint Equipment

11.8 A variety of materials are suitable for restraining palletised loads. These include chains, steelwire or fibre rope, webbing lashings and webbing or rope nets. Although the metal restraining devices may be stronger they are less convenient and require to be used with end attachments such as shackles, thimbles etc and unless the load is adequately protected it might be damaged, which could result in permanent distortion of the load and slackening of the restraint system.

11.9 Webbing lashing assemblies which incorporate special end fittings and tensioning devices are suitable for securing palletised loads to vehicles. The webbing is usually made from man-made fibres and has the property of being slightly elastic in use which helps to prevent the load from working loose. It is preferable to use webbing assemblies which are manufactured to the requirements of BS 5759.

11.10 Rope or webbing nets are suitable both for securing the cargo to the pallet and for securing the palletised load to the vehicle.

Restraining Methods

11.11 The restraining method adopted will depend on the type and size of the vehicle, the position and number of anchorage points and the size, weight and number of pallets in the load. However, the following principles should be followed for whatever scheme is chosen:

(i) Vertical and tipping motions should be prevented by a lashing placed across the top of the pallet load.

(ii) Lashings should be positioned to prevent movement of the pallets in any direction.

(iii) The pallet lashings should not be attached to or pass under, the strapping or binding used to secure the pallet to the cargo.

(iv) Where pallets are stacked, cross lashings must be such that each pallet of the top layer has at least one cross lashing. Any pallet which is above the general height of the load should have at least two cross lashings.

11.12 Dunnage may be used in some cases to assist in restraining the load. If the sideboards, headboard and tailboard are sufficiently strong and the pallets occupy all the vehicle platform space then dunnage alone may be sufficient to restrain the load horizontally, but some vertical restraint may be necessary. If pallets are stacked, however, additional lashings will be needed for the upper pallets.

SECTION 12. CONTAINERS

12.1 In this section the term 'container' is used to describe both a box type construction and an open frame structure enclosing the load or tank and which may in either case be lifted off the vehicle as a single unit comprising container and load. In many instances the advice on loading box type containers can be applied equally to vehicles with box van bodies.

ISO/BS CONTAINERS

12.2 The majority of containers in use are constructed to International (ISO 1496) or British (BS 3951) standards. A common feature in the construction of these containers is that specially designed corner castings are incorporated which can be used, in conjunction with twist locks fitted on the vehicle, to provide a simple and positive means of restraint (see Fig 22).

12.3 This type of container should normally be carried on vehicles fitted with twist locks. Twist locks must be maintained in serviceable condition and a minimum of four used for each container carried (see Section 5.9). Provided that the twist locks are fully engaged and locked in position, the container will be adequately secured and no further restraint will be necessary.

12.4 If carried on a vehicle not fitted with twist locks, a retention system must be used that fulfils the requirements set out in Sections 3—7.

OTHER TYPES OF CONTAINER

12.5 Containers which do not have the ISO type corner castings may be fitted with special attachment brackets or lashing rings. Safe methods for securing these containers will therefore vary according to the type being transported but the restraint system used must fulfil the requirements set out in Sections 3—7.

12.6 Containers should not project beyond the rear or sides of the vehicle loading platform because permanent distortion of the container may take place if part of its base is left unsupported.

12.7 Lashings or other securing devices should only be attached to those points on the container intended for the purpose, or for lifting or mechanical handling when laden, such as lashing rings or special brackets. All attachment points on the container should be examined to ensure that they are in sound condition and all the available attachment points should be used to secure it to the vehicle platform.

STOWAGE OF GOODS IN CONTAINERS

12.8 Incorrect loading of a container may result in dangerous situations occurring when the container is handled or transported; in addition serious damage may be caused to the goods carried. In many instances the driver will have no control over the packing of a container nor be able to inspect its contents when he accepts it for carriage. If it is apparent that the container has not been safely stowed then it should not be accepted.

12.9 Inadequate stowing arrangements within the container might result in the load shifting which could adversely affect the stability of the vehicle.

12.10 The following general stowage rules which affect road safety should always be observed:

a) The load should not exceed the permitted payload of the container;

b) The load should be evenly distributed across the floor area of the container. In no case should more than 60% of the load be in less than half the length of the container;

c) Heavy goods should not be stowed on top of lighter goods and wherever possible the centre of gravity of the loaded container should be below the mid-point of its height;

d) The load should be secured in the container against any reasonable forces which might be expected to occur during the journey. A tightly packed load will be less likely to move than one which has spaces between parts of the load;

e) After the packing of the container is completed, steps should be taken to ensure that the load and dunnage will not fall out when the doors are opened. Webbing lashings or nets are often suitable for this purpose, alternatively a timber or metal gate can be constructed.

12.11 More detailed information on the stowage of goods in containers can be found in British Standard BS 5073.

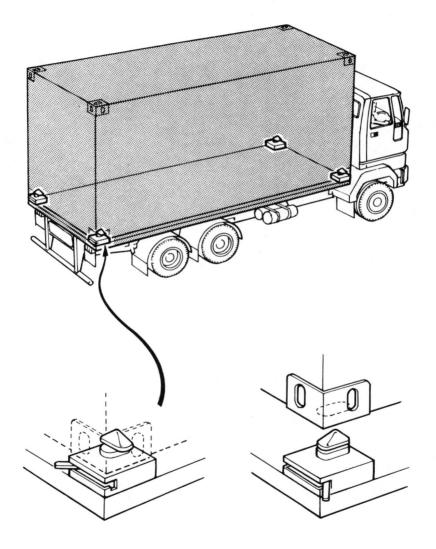

Figure 22

SECTION 13. ENGINEERING PLANT

13.1 This section provides guidance on the measures necessary for the safe carriage of tracked and wheeled engineering plant by vehicles constructed to comply fully with the Motor Vehicles (Construction and Use) Regulations 1978 and thereby permitted unrestricted use of the roads. It does not deal with the carriage of large machines etc on special purpose vehicles whose use on the roads is restricted by current regulations. However, the general advice contained in this section will apply in many cases.

13.2 Heavy engineering plant is normally transported on purpose built vehicles which are specifically designed to provide easy loading and unloading facilities and are usually provided with adequate anchorage points for attaching the lashings. Lighter engineering plant may in some circumstances be carried on general purpose vehicles. However, in these cases the method used to secure the load should provide equal security to that obtained by using purpose built vehicles.

13.3 High loads may endanger bridges etc over roads, so when these are carried it is essential that the driver knows the exact height of the load above the ground. Since loads with a high centre of gravity might seriously affect the vehicle's stability such items of engineering plant should only be transported on vehicles with a low platform height.

13.4 A wheeled or tracked vehicle must be lashed down in position on the carrying vehicle, with the parking brake applied. The effectiveness of the parking brake on its own will be limited by the frictional resistance between the vehicle and the deck of the carrying vehicle, and even in normal driving conditions this will be inadequate and the vehicle will therefore require additional restraint. This additional restraint should take the form of a lashing system and some arrangement whereby the load is prevented from moving either forward or to the rear by an obstacle (or obstacles) securely fixed to the vehicle which butt against the wheels or tracks or some other part of the equipment carried.

13.5 Engineering plant should be dismantled as far as is necessary to keep its overall dimensions within the length and width limits of the carrying vehicle. Where this is not possible then care should be taken that the conditions and restrictions contained in Regulation 140 of the Motor Vehicles (Construction and Use) Regulations 1978: SI 1978 No 1017, and the relevant provision of the Motor Vehicles (Authorisation of Special Types) General Order 1979: SI 1979 No 1198, concerning the carriage of wide or long loads are also complied with.

13.6 All moveable assemblies such as jibs, brackets, booms, slewing super structures and cabs etc must be left in the position recommended for transportation by their manufacturers and must be secured to prevent movement relative to the main body of the machine.

13.7 All hydraulic booms, arms etc, must be lashed down to prevent rising or slewing during transit.

13.8 When the machine has been stowed and the engine stopped, the pressure in the hydraulic system should be relieved by moving all of the control levers through all their positions. This operation should be done at least twice. Controls should be set so as to prevent movement of ancillary items during transit.

13.9 Bags, tool kits, or other heavy objects should not be left loose in the operator's cab of the plant being carried.

13.10 The positioning of the engineering plant and any of its detached assemblies must be so arranged that the legal axle weight limits are not exceeded and the safe handling of the vehicle is not impaired. The clearance between the undersides of low loading vehicles and the road surface should be checked before moving off (see Section 3 paragraph 6).

13.11 The machine should be positioned on the carrying vehicle's platform so that forward movement is prevented either by part of the main body of the vehicle, eg swan neck, step or headboard, or by an attached transverse member securely attached through the platform to the vehicle's chassis frame.

13.12 All items removed from the machine such as buckets, grabs, blades, shovels and lifting appliances should be lashed to the deck of the vehicle.

13.13 Wheeled and light tracked machines should be restrained so that the effect of bouncing caused by road shocks transmitted from the carrying vehicle and amplified by the machine's tyres or suspension units is minimised. Where possible the suspension unit of the machine should be locked and vertical movement limited by lashings or other means of restraint. Otherwise the machine's frame or chassis should be supported on blocks.

13.14 Unless the machine is supported, the full contact area of its tyres, tracks, or rolls should rest on the deck of the carrying vehicle. If the tracks extend outside the frame of the carrying vehicle then the machine's frame or chassis should be supported.

13.15 The machine should be restrained against forward, backward and sideways movement by chain or webbing lashings attached to anchorage points on the vehicle. All lashings should incorporate some form of tensioning device.

13.16 In deciding the number of anchorage points to be used when arranging a restraint system, the following factors should be considered:

(i) The need to position the machine to achieve the correct load distribution to meet the legal axle load requirements and to ensure that the vehicle's handling is not impaired;

(ii) The extent to which other load restraint features are incorporated in the design of the vehicle;

(iii) Whether the machine has wheels, tracks or rolls;

(iv) The weight of the machine to be carried.

However, there should never be less than four anchorage points used.

RESTRAINING DEVICES

13.17 Apart from specialised fixing devices, the selection of materials for use in tie down schemes for engineering plant will be limited to chains, steel wire rope, webbing and their associated tensioning and coupling devices.

13.18 Where a transverse beam is used as a baulk it should be securely fixed so that all loads imposed on it are transmitted to the carrying vehicle's chassis frame. Where individual wheels or rolls are chocked with blocks or scotches these must be robust enough to resist crushing and be securely attached to the vehicle's platform where possible.

13.19 The lashings or securing devices should only be attached to those parts of the engineering plant which are of sufficient strength to withstand the stresses likely to be imposed on them.

13.20 The loaded machine should be inspected after the vehicle has been driven for a short distance in order to check that no movement has taken place and that restraining devices are fully secure. Periodic inspections should be made during the course of the journey.

SUGGESTED TIE DOWN SCHEMES

13.21 The tie down schemes described in the following figures 23—31 and related schedules are typical systems which might be adopted for the securing of the various types of engineering plant. Variations to any of these schemes would be acceptable provided that all the basic safety precautions outlined earlier have been complied with. For simplicity the figures show mainly chains used for lashings but in practice other lashing materials may be substituted–see Section 5.

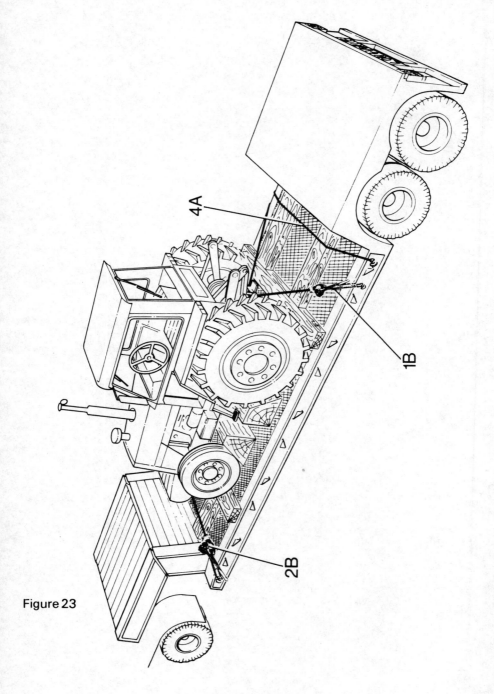

Figure 23

66

POSSIBLE HAZARD	PRECAUTION
1. Forward movement of machine	**A**. Front wheels butted against chocks against trailer bulkhead.
	B. Lashing chains from rear towing hook to anchorage points on trailer side members.
	C. Rear wheels butted against chocks.
2. Rearward movement of machine	**A**. Rear wheels butted against chocks against trailer bulkhead.
	B. Lashing from front axle or towing hook to anchorage points on trailer side members.
	C. Front wheels butted against chocks.
3. Sideways movement of machine	**A**. Restraint provided by lashings used for forward and rearward restraint.
4. Movement of ancillaries	**A**. Lashings across baulking to anchorage points on trailer side members.

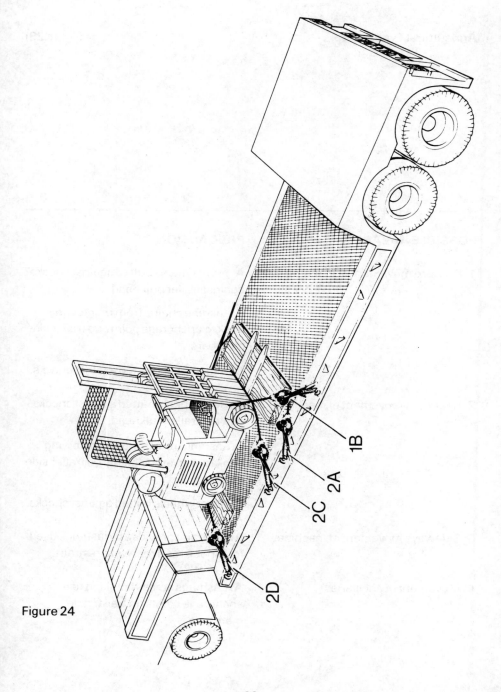

Figure 24

68

POSSIBLE HAZARD	PRECAUTION
1. Forward movement of machine	**A**. Rear wheels or counterweight of truck butted against chocks against trailer bulkhead. **B**. Lashing around the rear of the mast to anchorage points on trailer side members.
2. Rearward movement of machine	**A**. Front wheels of truck butted against chocks which are lashed to anchorage points on trailer side members. **B**. Forks lowered on to chocks and hydraulic pressure relieved by operation of controls twice with engine switched off. **C**. Lashings across the rear of the fork to the anchorage points forwards. **D**. Lashing from truck towing point to anchorage points on trailer side members.
3. Sideways movement of machine	**A**. Restraint produced by lashings used for forward and rearward restraint.

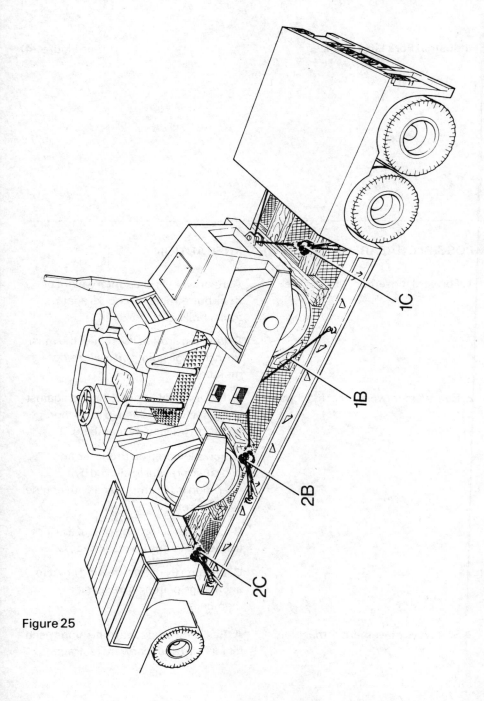

Figure 25

1C

1B

2B

2C

POSSIBLE HAZARD	PRECAUTION
1. Forward movement of machine	**A**. Front roll butted against chocks against trailer bulkhead.
	B. Lashing from frame and/or across member to anchorage points on trailer side members.
	C. Lashing from rear frame or towing hook to anchorage points on trailer side members.
2. Rearward movement of machine	**A**. Rear roll butted against chocks against trailer bulkhead.
	B. Lashing from frame and/or cross member to anchorage points on trailer side members.
	C. Lashing from front frame or towing hook to anchorage points on trailer side members.
3. Sideways movement of machine	**A**. Restraint provided by lashings used to prevent forward and rearward movement.

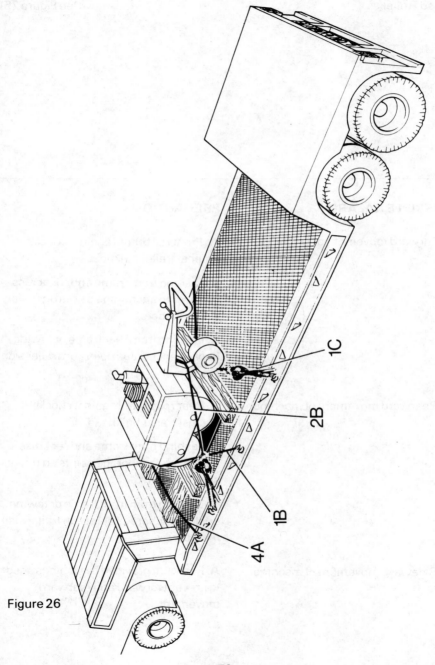

Figure 26

72

POSSIBLE HAZARD	PRECAUTION
1. Forward movement of machine	**A**. Front roll butted against chocks against trailer bulkhead.
	B. Lashing from and across the front of the machine body to anchorage points on trailer side members.
	C. Lashing around and across the rear of the rear wheel strut to anchorage points on trailer side members.
2. Rearward movement of machine	**A**. Rear roll butted against chocks.
	B. Lashing from and across the rear of the machine body to anchorage points on trailer side members.
3. Sideways movement of machine	**A**. Restraint provided by restraints to prevent forward and rearward movement.
4. Movement of ancillaries	**A**. Lashing across baulking.

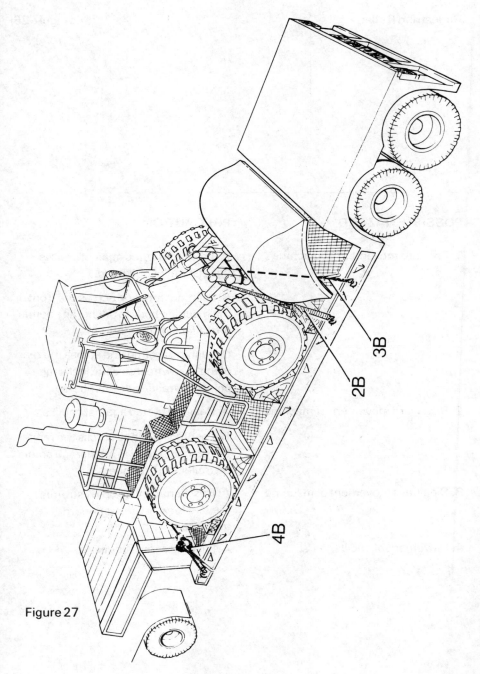

Figure 27

4B

2B

3B

POSSIBLE HAZARD	PRECAUTION
1. Articulation of front part of machine relative to rear part	**A**. Pivot locking bar bolted in position, in the case of pivot steer machines.
2. Movement of bucket assembly	**A**. Relieve hydraulic pressure in system by operating all controls twice, with the engine switched off.
	B. Lashings to secure bucket to the anchorage points on the trailer side members.
3. Forward movement of machine	**A**. Rear wheels butted against chocks against trailer bulkhead.
	B. Lashing from front axle or towing hook to anchorage points on trailer side members.
4. Rearward movement of machine	**A**. Front wheels butted against chocks.
	B. Lashing from rear axle or towing hook to anchorage points on trailer side members.
5. Sideways movement of machine	**A**. Restraint provided by lashings used to prevent forward and rear movement.

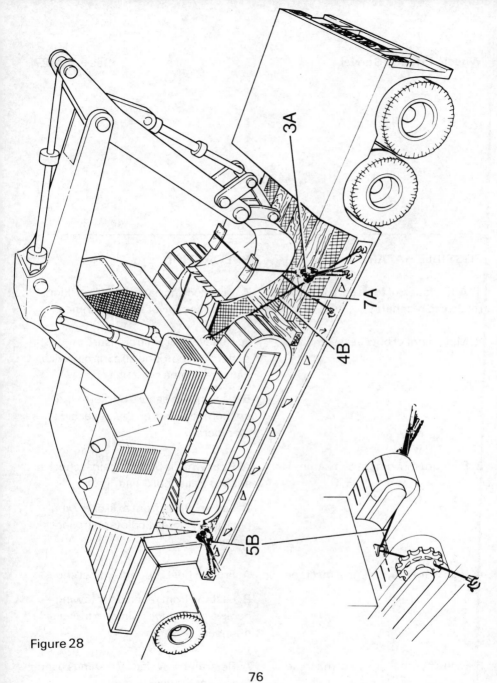

Figure 28

POSSIBLE HAZARD	PRECAUTION
1. Machine striking overhead obstruction	**A**. Stow equipment in position to give lowest overall height.
2. Movement of cab and super-structure relative to chassis of machine	**A**. Relieve hydraulic pressure by operating all controls twice, with engine switched off. **B**. Apply slew lock on slewing ring.
3. Movement of dipper arm away from stowed position	**A**. Lashing securing the bucket to anchorage points on the trailer side members.
4. Forward movement of machine	**A**. Tracks butted against the trailer bulkhead. **B**. Lashing chains from excavator front towing point or chassis cross member to anchorage points on trailer side members.
5. Rearward movement of machine	**A**. Tracks butted against chocks. **B**. Lashing chains from excavator rear towing point or chassis cross member through the idler sprocket to anchorage points on trailer side members.
6. Sideways movement of machine	**A**. Restraint provided by lashing chains used to prevent forward and rearward movement. Do not wedge heavy objects between the bucket and the machine chassis.
7. Movement of ancillaries	**A**. Lashings over baulkings.

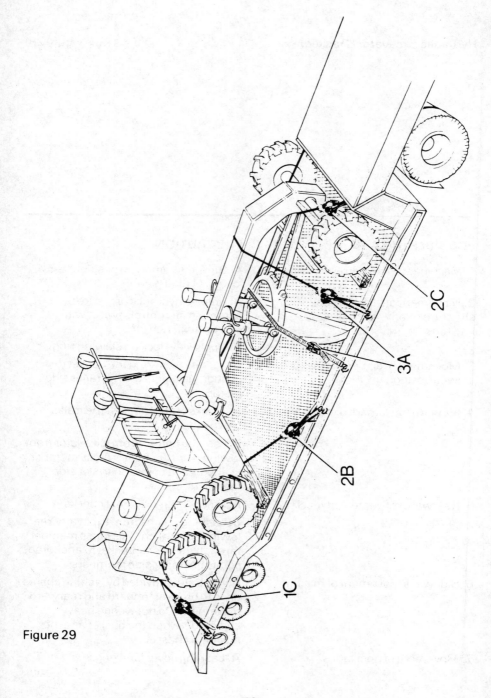

Figure 29

POSSIBLE HAZARD	PRECAUTION
1. Forward movement of machine	**A**. Blade and scarifier lowered to trailer deck.
	B. Front wheels butted against trailer bulkhead.
	C. Lashing from towing hook to anchorage points on trailer side members.
	D. Front wheels of tractor butted against chocks.
2. Rearward movement of machine	**A**. Rear wheels of tractor and front wheels of grader butted against chocks.
	B. Lashing from cross frame member to anchorage points on trailer side members.
	C. Lashing from front of mainframe to anchorage points on the trailer bulkhead.
3. Vertical movement of machine	**A**. Restraint provided by lashings over the mainframe and blade and those providing forward and rearward restraint.
4. Sideways movement of machine	**A**. Restraint provided by lashings used for other restraints.

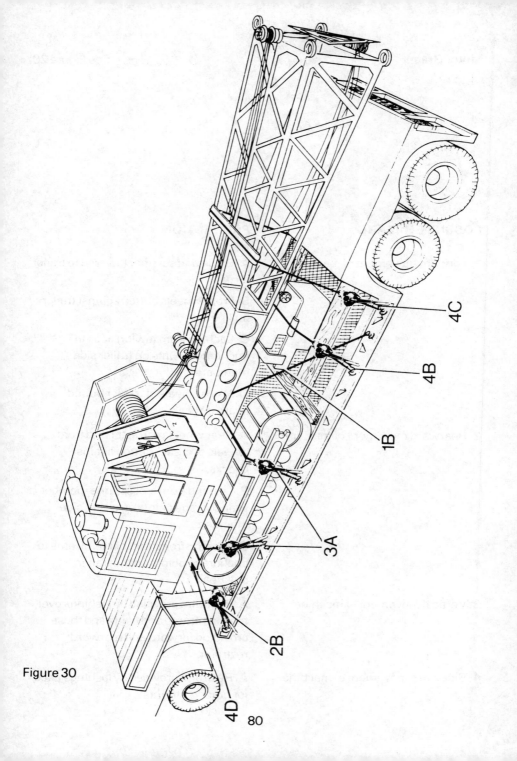

Figure 30

4C

4B

1B

3A

2B

4D

80

POSSIBLE HAZARD	PRECAUTION
1. Forward movement of machine	**A**. Tracks butted against chocks against trailer bulkhead. **B**. Lashing from chassis cross member or front towing hook to anchorage points on trailer side members.
2. Rearward movement of machine	**A**. Tracks butted against chocks against trailer bulkhead. **B**. Lashing from chassis cross member or rear towing hook to anchorage points on trailer side members.
3. Sideways movement of machine	**A**. Lashings over tracks to anchorage points on trailer side members. **B**. Restraint also provided by restraints for forward and rearward movement.
4. Movement of ancillaries	**A**. Break down boom and slew boom to rear and apply slew lock on slewing ring. **B**. Position bucket centrally on trailer and lash to anchorage points on trailer side members. **C**. Lower the jib onto the rear deck and lash to trailer side members. **D**. Support under counter-balance weights.

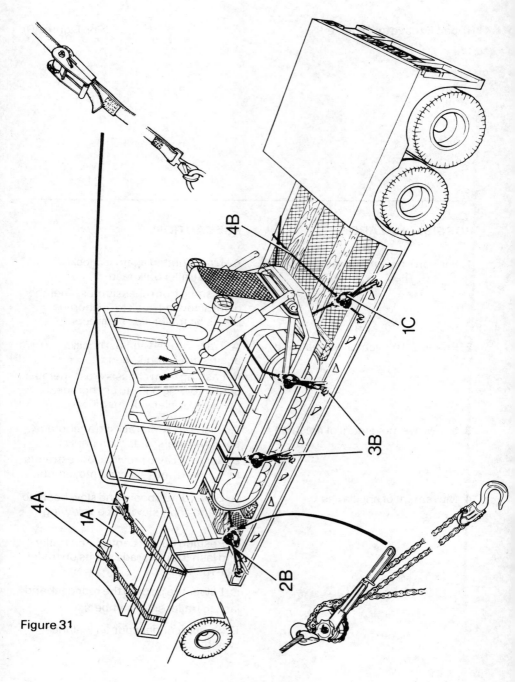

Figure 31

82

POSSIBLE HAZARD	PRECAUTION
1. Forward movement of machine	**A**. Dozer blade removed placed on front deck of trailer.
	B. Tracks butted against chocks against trailer bulkhead.
	C. Lashing from dozer blade U-frame trunnions to anchorage points on trailer side members.
2. Rearward movement of machine	**A**. Tracks butted against chocks against trailer bulkhead.
	B. Lashing from towing point to trailer side members.
3. Sideways movement of machine	**A**. Restraint provided by restraints to prevent forward and rearward movement.
	B. Lashings across tracks to anchorage points on trailer side members.
4. Movement of ancillaries	**A**. Dozer blade stowed on front deck. Lashing across blade to trailer side members.
	B. Lashing across baulking.

SECTION 14. CARRIAGE OF VEHICLES BY 'PIGGYBACK'

14.1 Vehicles and trailers should be carried on other vehicles that are suitable for that purpose with appropriate lashing points fitted and appropriate lashing equipment supplied. In general the securing arrangements should follow the same basic principles as suggested for the carriage of engineering plant in Section 13, but the additional points that follow should be noted.

14.2 The vehicle or trailer should be carried with the parking brake in the 'on' position, prefereably with the wheels chocked, and (where applicable) the transmission in neutral. If possible the chocks should be securely attached to the carrying vehicle's deck.

14.3 The vehicle or trailer being carried should be positioned so that its weight is fully supported by the carrying vehicle, so it is important to ensure that the carrying vehicle's deck is long enough to take the vehicle or trailer without excessive overhang. If necessary spreader plates should be used to avoid high localised loading–eg by the landing legs of a semi-trailer.

14.4 The restraint provided by the friction between the tyres and the deck with the parking brake on will not be sufficient to prevent movement so the vehicle or trailer being carried should be lashed to the carrying vehicle using appropriate lashing equipment as detailed in Section 5. A tensioning device should be used in each lashing and the lashings used to restrain the fore and aft movement should be set at an angle of less than $60°$ from the horizontal to obtain the maximum effect. The lashings should be tested for adequate tension after the vehicle has travelled a few miles and again at intervals during the journey and be retensioned if necessary.

14.5 Lashing should be made onto parts of the vehicle's or trailer's axles or chassis that are adequate for the purpose. Care should be taken to avoid straining or damaging other vehicle components such as brake pipes, hoses, electrical cables etc, through lashing over or near them.

14.6 The carriage of laden vehicles is not recommended but if this is necessary then extra attention should be paid to the resultant higher centre of gravity of the carrying vehicle and the possible consequential loss of stability when cornering or braking. It may also be necessary to put extra lashings onto the chassis of the vehicle or trailer being carried to pull it down on its springs and hence help to avoid an unstable load.

14.7 If more than one vehicle or trailer is carried in 'piggyback' fashion then each vehicle carried should be lashed to the one on which it rests and then all those carried should be lashed to the carrying vehicle.

14.8 All loose equipment on the vehicles or trailers being carried, and on the carrying vehicle, should be securely stowed.

14.9 An example of a recommended lashing arrangement is shown in Fig. 32.

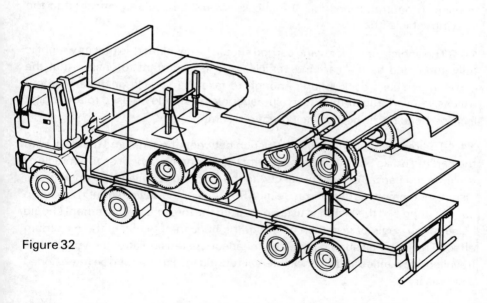

Figure 32

"Maintenance and use of vehicle so as not to be a danger

(1) A motor vehicle, every trailer drawn thereby and all parts and accessories of such vehicle and trailer shall at all times be in such condition, and the number of passengers carried by such vehicle or trailer, the manner in which any passengers are carried in or on such vehicle or trailer, and the weight, distribution, packing and adjustment of the load of such vehicle or trailer shall at all times be such that no danger is caused or is likely to be caused to any person in or on the vehicle or trailer or on a road.

Provided that in the case of a public service vehicle the provisions of this Regulation with regard to the number of passengers carried shall be deemed to be complied with if the number does not exceed that for the time being permitted by regulations made or having effect as if made under Section 148 of the 1960 Act with regard to the carrying capacity of public service vehicles.

(2) The load carried by a motor vehicle or trailer shall at all times be so secured, if necessary by physical restraint other than its own weight, and be in such a position, that neither danger nor nuisance is likely to be caused to any person or property by reason of the load or any part thereof falling or being blown from the vehicle or by reason of any other movement of the load or any part thereof in relation to the vehicle.

(3) No motor vehicle or trailer shall be used for any purpose for which it is so unsuitable as to cause or be likely to cause danger or nuisance to any person in or on the vehicle or trailer or on a road."

APPENDIX B REGULATIONS CONCERNING 'DANGEROUS GOODS' CARRIED BY ROAD VEHICLES

Order of Secretary of State (No 11) dated 20 September 1924, byelaws as to the conveyance of explosives on roads and in certain special cases–SRO 1924 No 1129.

The Conveyance of Explosives Byelaws 1951–S.I. 1951 No 869.

The Conveyance of Explosives Byelaws 1958–S.I. 1958 No 230.

The Conveyance by Road of Military Explosives Regulations 1977–S.I. 1977 No 888.

Poisons Rules 1970–S.I. 1970 No 798.

The Gas Cylinders (Conveyance) Regulations 1931–SRO 1931 No 679.

The Compressed Gas Cylinders (Fuel for Motor Vehicles) Conveyance Regulations 1940–SRO 1940 No 2009.

The Gas Cylinders (Conveyance) Regulations 1959–S.I. 1959 No 1919.

The Petroleum (Inflammable Liquids and other Dangerous Substances) Order 1947–S.I. 1947 No 1443.

The Petroleum Spirit (Conveyance by Road) Regulations 1957–S.I. 1957 No 191.

The Petroleum (Carbon Disulphide) Order 1958–S.I. 1958 No 257.

The Carbon Disulphide (Conveyance by Road) Regulations 1958–S.I. 1958 No 313.

The Petroleum Spirit (Conveyance by Road) Regulations 1958–S.I. 1958 No 962.

The Carbon Disulphide (Conveyance by Road) Regulations 1962–S.I. 1962 No 2527.

The Petroleum Spirit (Conveyance by Road) (Amendment) Regulations 1966–S.I. 1966 No 1190.

The Petroleum (Carbon Disulphide) Order 1968–S.I. 1968 No 571.

The Petroleum (Corrosive Substances) Order 1970–S.I. 1970 No 1945.

The Corrosive Substances (Conveyance by Road) Regulations 1971–S.I. 1971 No 618.

The Petroleum (Inflammable Liquids) Order 1971–S.I. 1971 No 1040.

The Inflammable Liquids (Conveyance by Road) Regulations 1971–S.I. 1971 No 1061.

The Inflammable Substances (Conveyance by Road) (Labelling) Regulations 1971–S.I. 1971 No 1062.

The Petroleum (Organic Peroxides) Order 1973–S.I. 1973 No 1897.

The Organic Peroxides (Conveyance by Road) Regulations 1973–S.I. 1973 No 2221.

The Dangerous Substances (Conveyance by Road in Road Tankers and Tank Containers) Regulations 1981–S.I. 1981 No 1059.

Health and Safety at Work etc Act 1974–ISBN 0 10 543774 3.

The Radioactive Substances (Carriage by Road) (Great Britain) Regulations 1974–S.I. 1974 No 1735.

The Radioactive Substances (Road Transport Workers) (Great Britain) Regulations 1970–S.I. 1970 No 1827.

The Radioactive Substances (Road Transport Workers) (Great Britain) (Amendment) Regulations 1975–S.I. 1975 No 1522.

Code of Practice for the Carriage of Radioactive Materials by Road (1982 Impression).

Northern Ireland only. The Radioactive Substances (Carriage by Road) Regulations (Northern Ireland) 1983–SR 1983 No 344.

European Agreement concerning the International Carriage of Dangerous Goods by Road (ADR).

Note: New comprehensive controls of all aspects of the conveyance by road of dangerous substances are being prepared by the Health and Safety Commission and the Department of Transport. Regulations dealing with road tankers and tank containers conveying dangerous substances were introduced in 1981. The

Classification, Packaging and Labelling of Dangerous Substances Regulations should be introduced in 1984 and be fully in force by 1986. These regulations will require all dangerous substances to be properly packaged and labelled both for supply and for conveyance by road. Proposals for Dangerous Substances (Conveyance by Road in Packages etc) Regulations were published as a Consultative Document in March 1984. These draft regulations are planned to replace the outdated existing legislation with more comprehensive controls. The Consultative Document included a draft approved Code of Practice which gives practical guidance on operational aspects of the conveyance by road of dangerous substances in packages etc.

APPENDIX C REGULATIONS CONCERNING THE
TRANSIT OF ANIMALS
BY ROAD VEHICLES

Conveyance of Live Poultry Order of 1919(10091).

The Transit of Animals (General) Order 1973–S.I. 1973 No 1377.

The Transit of Animals (Road and Rail) Order 1975–S.I. 1975 No 1024.

The Transit of Animals (Road and Rail) (Amendment) Order 1979–S.I. 1979 No 1013.

The Code of Practice on the care of farm animals and horses during their transport on roll-on/roll-off Ferries (Ministry of Agriculture and Fisheries and Food 1983).

Printed in the United Kingdom for The Stationery Office
J0015908 6/97 C6 G3397 10170